Grade 1

The Syllabus of Examinations should be read for details of requirements, especially those for scales, aural tests and sight-reading. Attention should be paid to the Special Notices on the front inside cover, where warning is given of changes.

The syllabus is obtainable from music dealers or from The Associated Board of the Royal Schools of Music, 14 Bedford Square, London WC1B 3JG (please send stamped addressed envelope measuring about 9×6 ins.).

In overseas centres, information may be obtained from the Local Representative or Resident Secretary.

REQUIREMENTS

SCALES AND BROKEN CHORDS (from memory)

Scales
major and minor (harmonic only): each hand separately, R.H. up and down (L.H. may, if the candidate prefers, be played down and up) in the following keys: C, G, D, F majors (two octaves); A minor (one octave); and in contrary motion with both hands beginning and ending on the key-note (unison), in the key of C major only (one octave).

Broken Chords
in the major keys of C, G & F, with each hand separately, starting from the lowest note (up and down), according to the example shown in the syllabus.

PLAYING AT SIGHT (see current syllabus)

AURAL TESTS (see current syllabus)

THREE PIECES

LIST A	page
1 **Leopold Mozart** (1719-1787) Menuet in D	3
2 **Thomas Attwood** (1763-1838) Sonatina No.3 in F: second movement	4
3 **Angus Morrison** (1902-1989) Lullaby, from *Pieces for Clio*	5

LIST B	
1 **Anon.** Corranto	6
2 **George Dyson** (1883-1964) Lullaby, from *Twelve Easy Pieces*	7
3 **Ferenc Farkas** Old Hungarian Dance	8

Candidates must prepare Nos. 1 & 2 from the *same* list, A or B, but may choose No.3 from *either* list or one of the further alternatives listed below:

F. Beyer   Andante in A minor, Op.101 No.60
S. Heller   Prelude in E minor, Op.119 No.9
These are included in More Romantic Pieces for Piano, Book I, *published by the Associated Board*

Editor for the Associated Board: **Lionel Salter**

A:1
MENUET in D

LEOPOLD MOZART

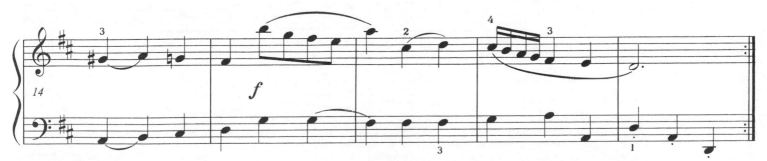

This is the seventh piece from the notebook Leopold Mozart wrote in 1759 for his 8-year-old daughter Nannerl; but her young brother Wolfgang (aged 4) almost immediately started playing it too! All dynamics and marks of articulation are editorial, and appoggiaturas are written out in the text.   L.S.

A:2
SONATINA No.3 in F
Second movement

Edited by
Richard Jones

ATTWOOD

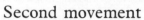

After studying in Naples, Thomas Attwood went to Vienna, where for two years he was a pupil of Mozart, who thought highly of his talents. On returning to England he became music-master to various members of the royal family, and later organist of St Paul's Cathedral. When the Royal Academy of Music was founded in 1823, he was one of its first professors: he became a great friend of young Mendelssohn. This sonatina comes from his *Easy Progressive Lessons* (c.1795): all dynamics and phrasing are editorial. L.S.

A:3
LULLABY
from 'Pieces for Clio'

ANGUS MORRISON

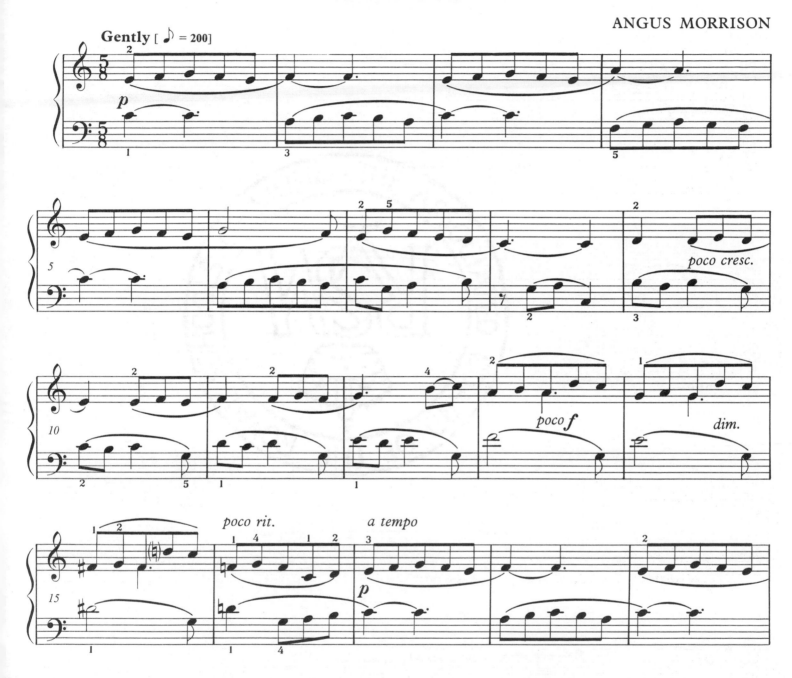

Angus Morrison was a pianist distinguished for his refined style and for his interpretation of early 20th-century French composers. For over 40 years he was a professor at the Royal College of Music. *Pieces for Clio* were written for his grand-daughter.   L.S.

B:1
CORRANTO

ANON.

This is No.204 of the *Fitzwilliam Virginal Book*, a collection of keyboard music copied by Francis Tregian the younger from 1609 to 1619 while in the Fleet Prison, charged as a recusant. A slightly different version of the piece also appears as No.193 under the title 'A Toy'. The original bar lengths have been halved; phrasing and dynamics are editorial. The final chord has been reduced for the benefit of candidates with small hands, who may also omit the bracketed note in bar 18.   L.S.

B:2
LULLABY
from 'Twelve Easy Pieces'

DYSON

Sir George Dyson taught at several leading public schools (including Marlborough, Rugby, Wellington and Winchester) before becoming director of the Royal College of Music (where he had himself been a student), a post he held for 14 years.   L.S.

B:3
OLD HUNGARIAN DANCE

FERENC FARKAS

Ferenc Farkas (pronounced Fe'rents Fawr'kosh) first studied in Budapest and then became a pupil in Rome of Respighi, who greatly influenced his style (as did Stravinsky), though he was also active as a folk-music collector. Much honoured in his own country, he has been a director of various conservatories, and for over a quarter of a century he taught composition in the Budapest Academy, where he trained many pupils later to become famous, including Ligeti. L.S.

Reprinted by permission, for use only in connection with the examinations of the Royal Schools of Music. All enquiries for this piece apart from the examinations should be addressed to Editio Musica Budapest, Vörösmarty tér 1, H-1370 Budapest.

AB 2245